Rank It!

STOCK CAR DRIVERS

MEGAN COOLEY PETERSON

WORLD BOOK
BOLT

This World Book edition of *Stock Car Drivers*
is published by agreement between
Black Rabbit Books and World Book, Inc.
© 2017 Black Rabbit Books,
2140 Howard Dr. West,
North Mankato, MN 56003 U.S.A.
World Book, Inc.,
180 North LaSalle St., Suite 900,
Chicago, IL 60601 U.S.A.

Design and Production by Michael Sellner
Photo Research by Rhonda Milbrett

Library of Congress Control Number: 2015954678

HC ISBN: 978-0-7166-9862-3   PB ISBN: 978-0-7166-9863-0

Printed in the United States at CG Book Printers,
North Mankato, Minnesota, 56003. PO #1791 4/16

CONTENTS

CHAPTER 1

Start Your ENGINES

A **stock car** rumbles to life. The green flag waves, and the driver steps on the gas pedal. The driver races past other cars. They all go around and around the track. Finally, the driver crosses the finish line first and wins.

Stock car drivers push speed to the limit. Turn the page, and find out where your favorite drivers rank.

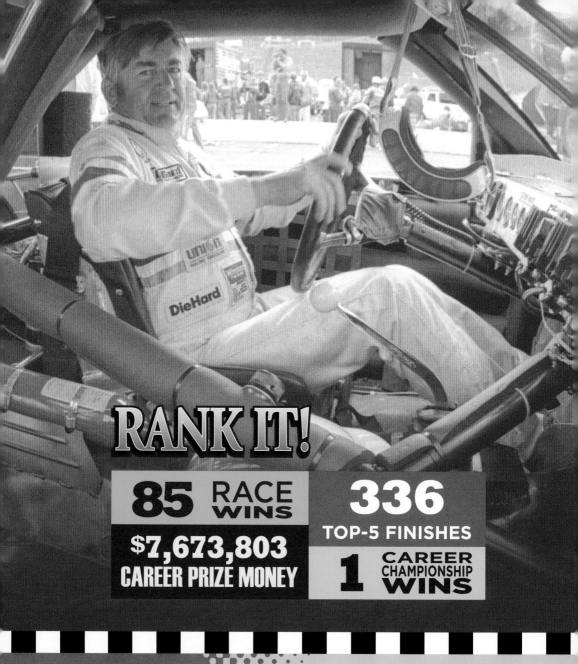

RANK IT!

85 RACE WINS	336 TOP-5 FINISHES
$7,673,803 CAREER PRIZE MONEY	1 CAREER CHAMPIONSHIP WINS

The Daytona 500 is the Super Bowl of stock car racing.

Most Daytona 500 Wins

Richard Petty	Cale Yarborough
7	4

CHAPTER 2

The

Bobby Allison
raced from 1961–1988

Bobby Allison sped around the track. It was the 1988 Daytona 500. At the checkered flag, Allison's car crossed the line first. He was the oldest driver to win the Daytona 500. And he was one of **NASCAR's** most popular drivers.

Bobby Allison	Dale Jarrett	Jeff Gordon
3	3	3

Dale Earnhardt
raced from 1975–2001

Dale Earnhardt pushed the limits of racing. At the 1987 **All-Star Race**, Bill Elliott bumped Earnhardt's car. Earnhardt slid into the grass. Instead of slowing down, he sped up. He took back the lead and won the race. Earnhardt's daring driving led him to seven championships.

RANK IT!

76 RACE WINS

$42,001,697 CAREER PRIZE MONEY

281 TOP-5 FINISHES

7 CAREER CHAMPIONSHIP WINS

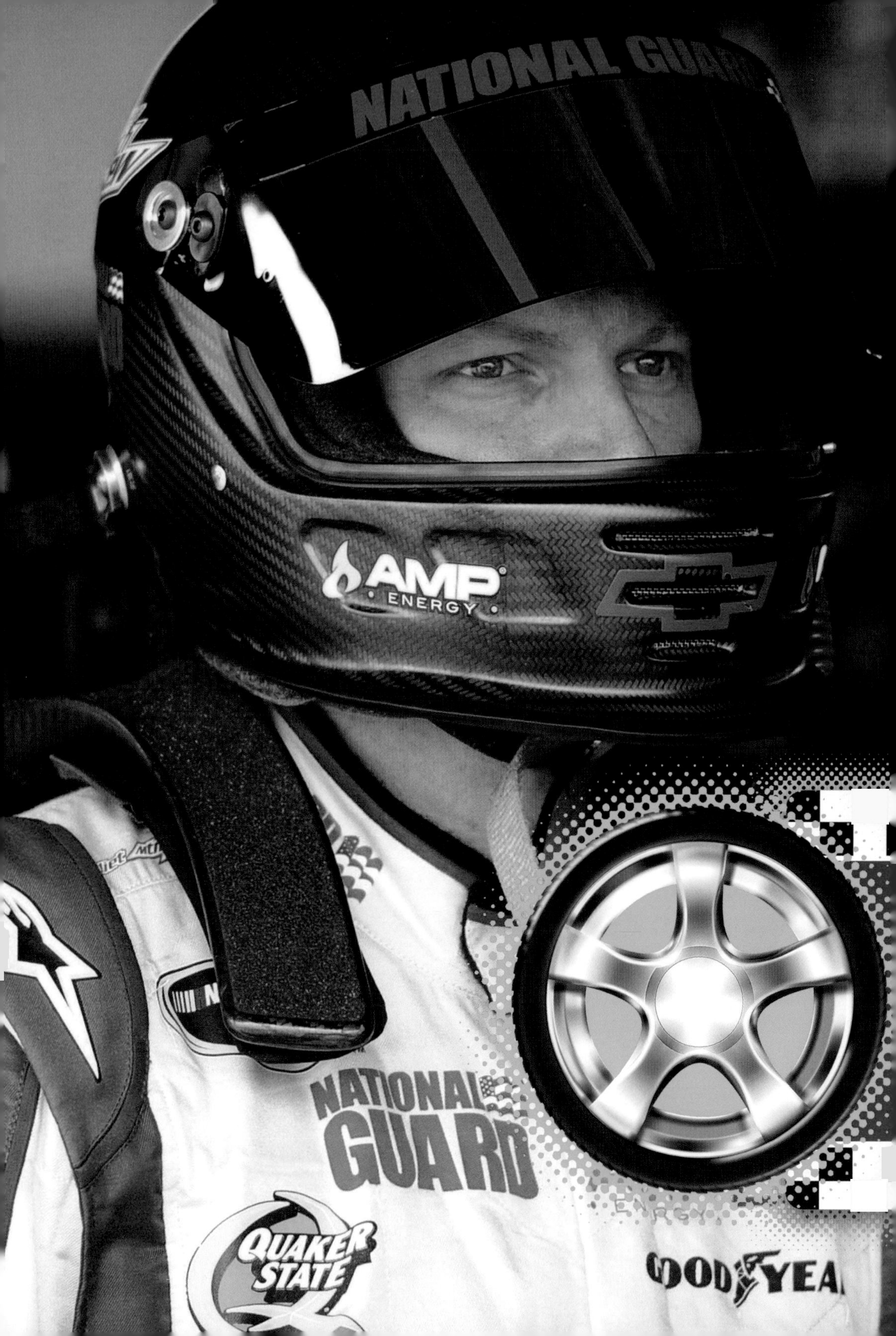
AMP
ENERGY
NATIONAL GUARD
QUAKER STATE

Dale Earnhardt Jr.
raced from 1999–present

Dale Earnhardt Jr. made history on May 20, 2000. He became the first **rookie** to win the All-Star Race. His father, Dale Earnhardt, joined him on victory lane. Junior also won the Daytona 500 in 2004 and 2014. Fans voted him their favorite driver 12 years in a row.

RANK IT!

26 RACE WINS

$95,680,982 CAREER PRIZE MONEY

143 TOP-5 FINISHES

0 CAREER CHAMPIONSHIP WINS

(through 2015)

Jeff Gordon
raced from 1992 to 2015

Jeff Gordon sped into NASCAR. He won Rookie of the Year in 1992. In 1995, he became the youngest driver to win the championship. Gordon won 13 races in 1998. Many consider him one of the greatest drivers of all time.

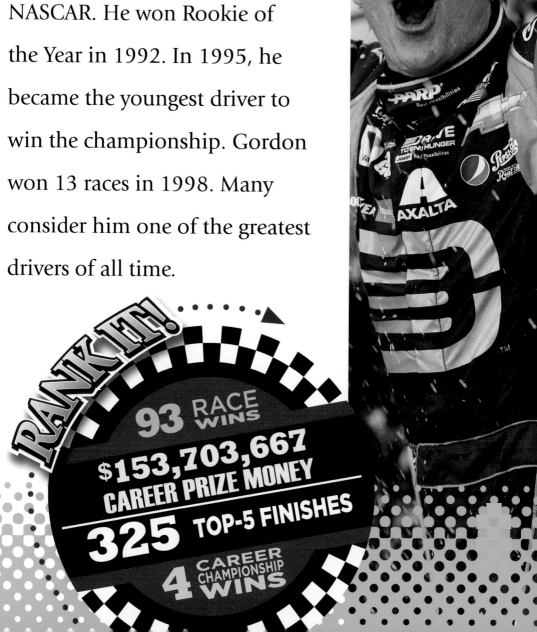

RANK IT!

93 RACE WINS

$153,703,667 CAREER PRIZE MONEY

325 TOP-5 FINISHES

4 CAREER CHAMPIONSHIP WINS

Richard Petty
raced from 1958–1992

Richard Petty could do almost anything with a race car. He set the record for most wins. He led more than 50,000 laps. In 2010, Petty entered the Hall of Fame. Stock car drivers will chase Petty for years to come.

RANK IT!

200 RACE WINS

555 TOP-5 FINISHES

$8,541,210 CAREER PRIZE MONEY

7 CAREER CHAMPIONSHIP WINS

STOCK CAR PARTS

PLASTIC WINDSHIELD

V8 ENGINE

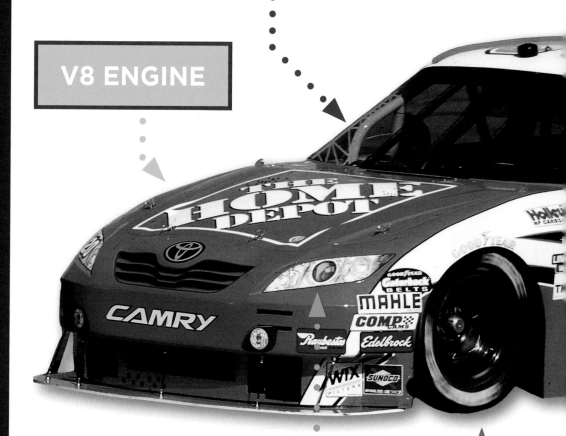

HEADLIGHT STICKERS

STEEL FRAME

COCKPIT

TIRES

20

HOME DEPOT
#2829

Jimmie Johnson
raced from 2001–present

Jimmie Johnson amazes fans with his high-flying driving. The Associated Press named him Male Athlete of the Year in 2009. He was the first NASCAR driver to earn that title. In 2010, he zoomed to his fifth straight championship. No other driver has won five titles in a row. In 2013, Johnson won a sixth title.

RANK IT!

75 RACE WINS

$150,926,713 CAREER PRIZE MONEY

207 TOP-5 FINISHES (through 2015)

6 CAREER CHAMPIONSHIP WINS

Danica Patrick
raced from 2012–present

Danica Patrick had a fast car at the 2013 Daytona 500. She raced the fastest **qualifying** lap. Patrick won the **pole**. She finished eighth in the race. No woman has placed higher at Daytona. Fans can't wait to see what Patrick does next.

RANK IT!

0 RACE WINS

$12,398,049 CAREER PRIZE MONEY

0 TOP-5 FINISHES

0 CAREER CHAMPIONSHIP WINS

(through 2015)

steering wheel
can be easily removed to help driver get out after a crash

racing suit
keeps driver safe during a fire

harness
stops driver from flying out of car

helmet ◀ ·····
protects
driver's
head

support
keeps head
and neck steady

window net ·······
keeps garbage
out of car

David Pearson
raced from 1960–1989

David Pearson had an eye for racing. Nicknamed the Silver Fox, he won 11 races in 1973. He only drove in 18 races that year. He also cruised to three championships. Many fans consider Pearson one of the best of all time.

RANK IT!

105 RACE WINS

$2,836,220 CAREER PRIZE MONEY

301 TOP-5 FINISHES

3 CAREER CHAMPIONSHIP WINS

Flags of
NASCAR

GREEN

START OF THE RACE

YELLOW

SLOW DOWN

RED

STOP FOR SAFETY REASONS

WHITE

ONE LAP LEFT IN RACE

CHECKERED
**WINNER CROSSES
THE FINISH LINE**

Tony Stewart
raced from 1999–present

Tony Stewart blazed onto the NASCAR stage. Known for his hot temper, he won Rookie of the Year. He went on to win three championships.

Stewart owns Stewart-Haas Racing. His driver Kevin Harvick won the championship in 2014. Danica Patrick also drives for Stewart.

48 RACE WINS

182 TOP-5 FINISHES

$122,231,607 CAREER PRIZE MONEY

3 CAREER CHAMPIONSHIP WINS

(through 2015)

Rusty Wallace
raced from 1980–2005

When Rusty Wallace hit the track, he became a fan favorite. He won at least one race 16 years straight. This is the third-longest winning streak in NASCAR. Wallace also won Rookie of the Year.

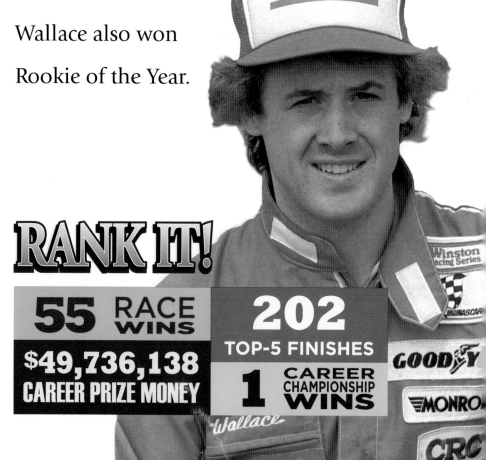

RANK IT!

55 RACE WINS

$49,736,138 CAREER PRIZE MONEY

202 TOP-5 FINISHES

1 CAREER CHAMPIONSHIP WINS

Cale Yarborough
raced from 1957–1988

Cale Yarborough couldn't wait to fly down the track. He lied about his age to start racing. Yarborough won championships in 1976, 1977, and 1978. He was the first driver to win three straight titles.

RANK IT!

83 RACE WINS

$5,646,479 CAREER PRIZE MONEY

255 TOP-5 FINISHES

3 CAREER CHAMPIONSHIP WINS

CHAPTER 3

Career Prize Money

MILLIONS OF DOLLARS

$150
$125
$100
$75
$50
$25
$0

$153,703,667*
$150,926,713*
$122,231,607*
$95,680,982*
$49,736,138

| Jeff Gordon | Jimmie Johnson | Tony Stewart | Dale Earnhardt Jr. | Rusty Wallace |

Race Wins

200 Richard Petty

105 David Pearson

93 Jeff Gordon*

RANK IT!

See if your favorites are up to the chase.

*as of 2015

Dale Earnhardt	Danica Patrick	Richard Petty	Bobby Allison	Cale Yarborough	David Pearson
$42,001,697	$12,398,049*	$8,541,210	$7,673,803	$5,646,479	$2,836,220

TOP-5 FINISHES

555 RICHARD PETTY   **336 BOBBY ALLISON**   **325 JEFF GORDON***

Championship Wins   1 Car = 1 Win

DALE EARNHARDT

RICHARD PETTY

JIMMIE JOHNSON*

GLOSSARY

All-Star Race (AL-STAR RAYS)—an annual NASCAR race held for drivers who have won at least one race in the current or previous season

NASCAR—National Association for Stock Car Auto Racing; NASCAR oversees many auto racing events.

pole (POHL)—the starting position in a race; drivers must win the qualifying round to start in the pole position.

qualifying (KWAL-uh-fy-ing)—the timed laps drivers run before a race to earn a starting spot in the race

rookie (ROOK-ee)—a first-year player

stock car (STAHK KAR)—a car for racing that is made from a regular model sold to the public

BOOKS

Challen, Paul. *NASCAR Racing.* Checkered Flag. New York: PowerKids Press, 2015.

Mason, Paul. *Stock Cars.* Motorsports. Mankato, MN: Amicus, 2010.

Niver, Heather Moore. *Racing's Greatest Records.* Greatest Records in Sports. New York: PowerKids Press, 2015.

WEBSITES

NASCAR
www.nascar.com/en_us/sprint-cup-series.html

Quiz! NASCAR Trivia
www.kidzworld.com/quiz/4479-quiz-nascar-trivia

INDEX